This book belongs to

....

First published in Hong Kong in 2010.
Second edition published in Hong Kong in 2011.
This edition published in Hong Kong in 2013.

ISBN 978-988-19134-1-8

Text copyright © Joanne O'Callaghan
Illustrations copyright © Ralph Kiggell
Designed by Seline Wu

Printed and bound in China by Everbest Printing Co. Ltd. Printed using woodfree paper and chlorine free bleaching.

For Sophia and Xavier

Jasper and Chelsey

My Hong Kong

by Joanne O'Callaghan

Illustrated by Ralph Kiggell

PEAK PUBLISHING

Hong Kong is a busy place,
Busy people, busy pace,
Shiny buildings fill the sky,
People walking, rushing by.

So let's explore where I belong —
Yes, let me show you my Hong Kong!

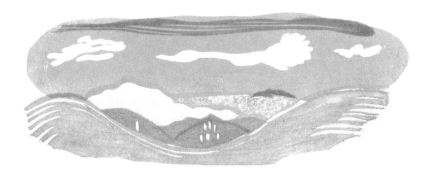

Let's catch the Peak Tram up the hill,
And up, and up — it's quite a thrill!
And in the garden at the top,
We'll run on grass and never stop.

Let's hike along the Dragon's Back!
Our Dads can carry us on the track.
We'll look for bugs and butterflies,
And kites that soar up in the skies.

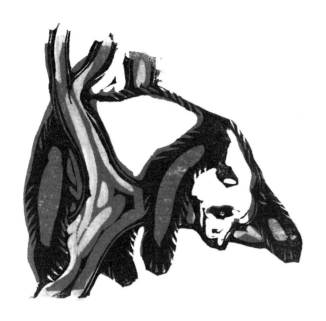

Let's see the Chinese panda bears
At Ocean Park – we must go there!
Their fur is all in black and white,
That's all they wear both day and night.

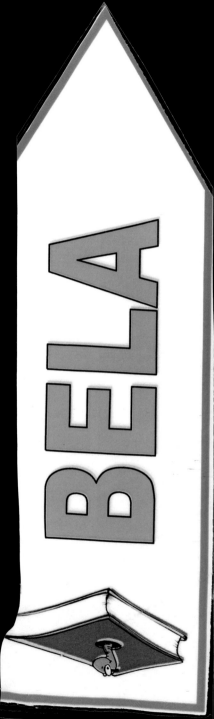

BELA

Let's ride the great Star Ferry, too!
Across the water to Kowloon.
We'll see the city as we float
And in the harbour, count the boats.

Let's stop for lunch at City Hall
And order dim sum for us all.
The ladies bring the little treats
On squeaky trolleys to our seats.

Let's have some fun in Hong Kong Park,
And watch the turtles 'til it's dark.
We'll feed the fish, some white, some red,
Then hurry home in time for bed.

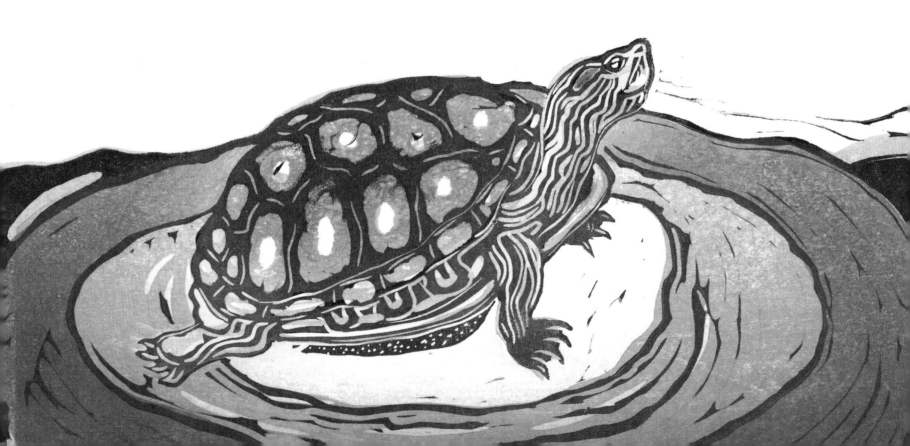

Let's go to Stanley on the bus,
The double-decker's fun for us!
Past Happy Valley and Repulse Bay,
We'll bump along the winding way.

Let's take our buckets and spades today,
We're off to South Bay Beach — hooray!
And where the water meets the land,
We'll build our castles in the sand.

Let's stay inside to play today,
Until the typhoon blows away.
We'll jump in puddles, when it's done,
On Bowen Road, where we can run.

Let's hang our paper lanterns out
When autumn leaves are all about.
We'll watch the dance the dragons do,
And eat our Moon Cakes, me and you.

Let's have a costume party, too.
I'll be a fairy — how about you?
On Pottinger Street, we'll climb the stairs
And find the masks we'd like to wear.

Let's stay up late to watch the lights,
At Chinese New Year, twinkle bright.
And at this special time of year,
The fireworks BANG for all to hear!

Yes, Hong Kong is a special place
With parks and trails, and open space.
Temples, a zoo, the big Buddha, too,
There's so much more to see and do.

So hurry back another day
To my Hong Kong, where we can play!